When Kids Achieve

WHEN KIDS ACHIEVE

Positive Monologues for Preteen Boys and Girls

Raf Mauro

Dramaline Publications

Dramaline Publications, 36-851 Palm View Road, Rancho Mirage, CA 92270
Phone: 619/770-6076, Fax : 619/770-4507, E-mail: drama@cyberg8t.com

Library of Congress Cataloging-in-Publication Data
Mauro, Raf.
    When Kids Achieve: Positive monologues for preteen boys and girls.
    / Raf Mauro.
        p. cm.
    Summary: A collection of monologues to celebrate achievement and promote self-esteem, arranged by the gender of the speaker.
    ISBN 0-940669-37-4 (alk. paper)
    1. Achievement motivation—Juvenile literature.
    2. Recitations—Juvenile literature. [1. Monologues. 2. Self-   esteem.]
    I. Title.
    BF504.3.M38   1997
    812'.54—dc21   97-18324

Cover design by John Sabel

This book is printed on 55# Glatfelter acid-free paper, a paper that meets the requirements of the American Standard of Permanence of paper for printed library material.

CONTENTS

FOREWORD	vii
A Writer Like My Dad?	3
Take Two and Hit to . . . Anywhere.	5
It's Not Magic or a Miracle. Okay, Maybe It's a Miracle.	7
Hula Hoops? No Way! Yes, Way!	9
Stop! Drop! And Roll!	10
This Kind of Thing Could Happen to Anybody	12
Do, Re, Me, Fa . . . Ah, You Know . . .	13
The Only Thing We Didn't Do Was Kiss the Blarney Stone	14
I Know Where Carmen San Diego Is	16
Not a Typical Day at the Mall	18
You Always Wind Up Back at School	20
It Seemed Like the Right Thing to Do	22
What's the Big Deal? Find Some Dirt, Seeds and Water.	24
Just Sign It	25
I Know, I Know . . . That's How I Am	26
Put Your Mind Where Your Mouth Is	27
They Call Me a Hero, but It's Just Common Sense to Me	31
When Is It Ever Enough?	33
The Biz There's No Biz Like	34
I Hope You Like It, I Made It	35
Nothing Special . . . Just Camp	36
Just a Line on a Graph	37
Nothing but Very Cold, Hard Water, Everywhere	38
Okay, He's a Guy, but He Knew What to Do	40
On Your Marks. Get Set. Bang. Run Like the Wind.	41
Not Re-Acting? Try It, You'll Like It.	43
I Think I Found a Way to Make Some Money	45
Sunday Morning in the Rain	46
Orginization Is the Name of the Game	48
It's Not the Debating Team	49
Stay Tuned for the News	51
ABOUT THE AUTHOR	55

FOREWORD

When I was asked to write this book, it occurred to me that one of the most important, and overlooked, resources we have as a nation, or as a world population, is the achievements of children. When kids achieve, the world is a better place. Not just for that time, but forever. The effects are lasting. When a child's self-esteem goes up and habits of achieving are set, society is better off, the child who achieves is better off, we are *all* better off.

When children, regardless of age or area of attempt, are trying something beyond their normal sphere, we must support them. Not do it for them, but give them the cheerleading that is appropriate, and acknowledgment afterward regardless of the outcome. We must applaud the effort, if nothing else. Eventually, the acknowledgment won't be necessary and the kids will stop seeking approval because they will approve of themselves. Internally referred approval is most profound. In the beginning, especially, support and acknowledgment are a must—and a win-win situation for us all. And when the habits of achievement are set in childhood, they are usually carried over to adulthood, making for a better society.

Please remember, the seeds of achievement are usually sown in the imagination. Where imagination stops, limits start. Encourage imagination.

RAF MAURO

GIRLS

A WRITER LIKE MY DAD?

Hi, my name is Amanda. They wanted me to come out here and tell you what I just did. I'm not sure why. Maybe it's because I'm so, like, young. I hope it's not because I'm a girl and they think that only boys can do this stuff. Anybody can do this. So, like, I wrote this thing, this movie script. How it happened was, I was just kickin' one Saturday and listening to my dad's friends read what they had written. There is this, like, meeting, kind of a party, too, the second Saturday of every month. It's called The Second Saturday in the Month Writers' Group. They read and drink wine and eat. Sometimes they let me sing for them. About a month ago, I get this idea for a movie, so I write this stuff down, okay? Like after school, in school, on the weekends. It's cool. It's like it's writing itself. Anyway, I get done what they call a first draft, and I show it to my dad. He's been a writer forever. He liked it! He got it! So he says, "Maybe you could read it next Saturday and get some feedback from the other writers." I just wanted *him* to go over it, not all those other writers. He said it would be cool and I should do it, and then he said to leave out all this stuff about camera angles and stuff like that. He said not to worry about that because that was the director's job. I'm thinking, Whoa, a director, it's not even finished yet.

So, like, Saturday comes and the writers show up and they eat and talk about boring grown-up stuff. Then they start reading what they'd written. Poems, short stories, a book proposal, and it's getting later and later and I'm getting two kinds of nervous: nervous that they won't get to me and nervous that they will. Dad says, "Okay, after the break, Amanda's got something she wrote." Now I was only one kind of nervous. Big-time. Blurry-eyed, dry-throat nervous.

Break is over, I get up to read. Dad tells them to be quiet. I die a little and get up and read. I read all the parts. My throat is okay. I can see the words and I get, like, really into it. I hear a laugh at the right time, a cough now and then, and when I look up as I turn a page, they're all staring at me. Way weird. So I stop, because other people want to read, too, and they're all saying, like, "Don't stop!" "What happens to the little girl?" They had been really listening. Cool. When I finished up to where I'd stopped writing, they all came over to talk to me about the plot and stuff. They had all kinds of advice and tips. I was floating. It was like I was in a room full of gauze, or clouds. Finally they all went back to the other writers' stuff and I went to the kitchen for some water. Mom grabbed me and gave me the hug of my life. I was smothered, crushed, mashed.

She told me how proud of me she was and how proud Daddy looked when I was reading and how these old, cynical writers never say anything nice to other writers unless they really mean it. Knocked me out. Later I was playing video games with some of my friends, but I couldn't concentrate. I mean, what if I can actually do this stuff?

TAKE TWO AND HIT TO . . . ANYWHERE!

They say that hitting a baseball is the hardest thing to do in all of sports. If you do it three out of every ten times it's, like, you're a big star. Whoever thought of that was way right. I can shoot a basketball. I was on the field hockey team at school until I pulled a hamstring. Water polo is supposed to be a tough, man's sport. Please. I played it with some of my home girls last summer, handled it. I can dance, I do my friends' hair, I get good grades—lots of stuff that I'm too cool to bring up. Okay? Okay. I don't reek.

So I tried out for Little League a few whiles ago, and like I was way out of place. First of all, the boys all resented me. The coach knew he had to accept girls and he picked me 'cause I was the only one left. So there I am on a team and on the bench for, like, a millennium. I play sometimes . . . it's a rule. Then this old woman who hangs out at the park and feeds the pigeons, little flying rats, starts talking to me. She told me I was standing wrong. This little old lady who could hardly stand up was telling *me* I was standing wrong? Please. But I was desperate, so. . . . Anyway, for about nine or ten days straight, before practice, after practice, she worked with me on my hitting. But I just couldn't get it. I kept striking out. The boys would tease me. "Hey, go home and bake some cookies!" "Yeah, go bake some cooties and snot-cookies!" That was Arthur Giovanetti. He's a total spaz-dork. One day after practice I asked Lena, that's the woman's name, what made her such an expert. She said, "I played professional baseball when I was young. Maybe you saw the movie, *A League of Their Own*, with Tom Hanks." That was way cool! Like, wow! She was a pro. That was a good movie. So, again, she tells me to get the bat head through the strike zone, where to make contact, how to wait on the ball, use my hips, all the good junk.

Now Saturday comes around and Billy Jantz doesn't show up and I get put into the starting lineup. First time up I actually hit a foul ball, hard. First time that ever happened. Second time up I walk. First time I ever got to first. Then Arthur got a double and I scored. Another first. Next time, we're behind by one run and there's one out, a man on first, and I'm up. The guys on the bench are all, like, looking at the ground and spitting. Boys do that a lot. Lena comes up behind the batting cage and says, "Lavonne, you can do this. Relax and wait on the pitch, don't lunge." The pitcher fires and I'm going to take the pitch but it was too juicy, so, I swung. Whack! It goes past the pitcher's head and into center field. The runner goes from first and the outfielder bobbles the ball and the runner scores and I wind up on second. Lena is jumping up and down, kinda. Hey, she's old, okay?

What a day! Arthur knocks me in with a single and here I am scoring the winning run! A few days later, Lena said that all I needed was a little encouragement and for someone to believe in me. I still know her. She's teaching me how to paint. She's, like, my best friend.

IT'S NOT MAGIC OR A MIRACLE.
OK, MAYBE IT'S A MIRACLE.

See this? Watch! (*She does a little dance step and twirls around*) I couldn't do that six months ago. I couldn't do anything six months ago except say . . . "It hurts, make it stop hurting!" I was, totally, what's the word? Oh yeah . . . incapacitated. A long time to be in bed. I was riding my bike and hit a hole and went down and totally messed up my spine. They operated. They put me in this full body cast. They said I probably wouldn't walk again. That is unless some breakthrough in medical science happened. Somehow I just, like, didn't believe them.

One day I was watching TV and a head popped through the door. It was my Uncle Ray. He lives about two thousand miles from here, but he came when he heard about the accident. He started telling me stuff about how the body knows how to heal itself, that there were ways to cure things that the doctors don't know about. Then he gave me a book about a man who was sent home from the hospital to die because the doctors said they couldn't do any more for him. They said his heart would give out in six months. That was twenty-five years ago and the man is still alive. Then Uncle Ray started to go through a bunch of, I don't know, phrases, I guess. He said that everything is possible as long as you can get all the negative stuff out of the way that stops the possible from being.

I didn't want to be a veggy the rest of my life, so I started to do what he said. Now he made me promise that I wouldn't tell anybody, even my parents, what it was. He came to the house every day. We'd sit there and go over this stuff day after day. He said nothing happens overnight. Then, one day, it was like duh, I finally got it.

When the cast came off, they gave me a brace. The brace was supposed to be on me forever. About two months ago, me and Uncle Ray took off the brace. And he started staying longer, sleeping over and helping me with the mental exercises.

Then it happened! I got up and walked a little. Just a step or two. Then the next day, a step or two more. Two days later I walked half way across the room. In a few weeks I did more.

Then, one day, my big sister started, by accident, a fire in the bathroom with, like, hair rollers. Ya know what? I got scared and actually ran out of the house! Everybody was staring at me. I didn't realize what I had done.

So here I am. And thanks to Uncle Ray, I'll be able to help somebody else.

HULA HOOPS? NO WAY! YES, WAY!

My sister Gracie is so way cool, I mean, totally together. I try to do what she does, dress like she dresses and talks and studies. She's totally awesome. She's six years older and a beauty. See, all my friends totally hate their older sibs. Marsha can't stand her brother Ralph. Well, okay, he's cute but she's his sister so he's a dweeb. And Savandra doesn't get along with Martique and on and on and on. So boring. Gracie does my homework with me, teaches me how to fix my hair. Now here's the kicker: When I told her I was coming here, she said, "Let's make you an outfit." We made this together. (*She models it*) Cool, right?

Gracie's birthday is next week. She's going to be eighteen. So yesterday I tried to think up a really cool birthday gift for her. But she already has everything and I have no money. So I was looking around in the attic and I found some Hula Hoops that Mom had when she was my age. Or maybe they were grandma's. So I figured I could cover three of them with these big sheets of paper Dad uses at work to wrap these things he's always shipping to Hong Kong. Then arrange them over her bed and write a poem on them and decorate them with flowers. Now don't say anything because it's like a big surprise. I already wrote the poem. This is it. Wanna hear it? It's called *Thank You, Gracie, Because.* "Thank you, Gracie, because when I'm sad, you always make me glad with your great big smile, and for always being there, / Thank you for helping me do my homework and giving me hints and tips on life and how to do my hair, / Thank you for letting me borrow everything you own—that can't break—and showing me how to live with flair. / I hope these hula hoops are big enough to show you the thank-yous in my heart, / I hope you also totally realize that for me these thank-yous are just a start."

The end.

STOP! DROP! AND ROLL!

Well, it was quite a Monday. I mean, like, it was a week in a day. Coming home from school Monday, I walked past the old nursery/day-care center I used to go to when I was little. I stopped in and Mrs. Brooks was still there. She was a lot older than I remembered, and was walking with a walker. Plastic hip. While I was sitting in her office telling her about my life, kids kept coming in. One kid had a bloody nose 'cause he was hit by another kid, another had scraped her knee . . . stuff like that. Then the phone rang and she answered it. Her face went white. When she hung up she was almost crying. "My oldest son was in a car crash, he's hurt badly, can you stay here and watch the office until Mrs. Phillips gets back?" I said it was cool, and she was out of there.

So I'm sitting there and one of the children-taker-care-ofs comes in and asks where Mrs. Brooks is. When I tell her what happened, she goes, "Great, now what am I supposed to do?" Then she said, "You look strong, would you mind helping me lift a cabinet off a child who's stuck behind it?"

We run over, and sure enough this boy is stuck behind a cabinet. We pushed and pulled and finally get the kid out. Then, just as I sat down to catch my breath, someone yelled, "Fire!" Oh God! So we run over to the classroom building I used to take naps in, and, sure enough, smoke is pouring out. A lady comes out and says that kids are inside and that the smoke is too thick for them to see to get out. I said, "Call 911!" and ran inside.

I got down on my belly and crawled to the kids. They were, like, terrified. So I told them what I'd learned when I went there, "Stop! Drop! And Roll!" It took a little convincing, but when I demonstrated, they all got it. Thank God. One by one I rolled them along the floor to the door, and got them out of the room. Some of them were coughing and some were crying. By then the smoke was so thick I almost panicked. But I maintained and started to crawl to the door. But . . . no door! It was hot and I was coughing and I was desperate.

Then I saw them through the smoke—two very big boots with very big feet in them belonging to a very big fireman. Thank God. What a day.

If someone had taught the kids Stop! Drop! And Roll! . . . none of this would have happened.

THIS KIND OF THING COULD HAPPEN TO ANYBODY

Can you make a funny noise? Bark like a dog? A real dog? How about some other tricks? You can win a lot of money on TV. One of the things I always liked to do was sing. Well, not real singing, actually, just mouthing the words to songs on the radio. Only when I do it, I work up a whole act and make up costumes and perform for other kids and my family and their friends.

I worked up this one thing, this is awesome, an Elton John thing. Remember him? My folks like him. He's got these weird clothes and weird glasses. So I made up this act and learned how to mimic him and did his "Rocket Man" for my friends and family. They all laughed a lot and my Uncle Sy said I should go on TV. Then, Aunt Helen said that they were auditioning for a local show called "Our Goofy Neighbors."

So I went down to audition for the show and there were, like, a zillion people there, all dressed really weird. I'm thinking, I don't have a chance. As if. But I wait.

When my turn comes and I step on the stage, the lights hurt my eyes and they start to tear up like I was totally crying. Then my music starts and I'm doing my Elton John thing with tears pouring down my face. I thought they would throw me out for sure, but the tears made the whole thing even funnier and people were laughing their heads off. I got picked to do the show. Awesome.

On show day, my whole family is in the audience. My turn comes and I step on stage and the lights hurt my eyes and they start to tear up as I start my Elton John thing and the audience loves it. Next thing I know, they're voting by applause and my family is practically knocking down the TV studio. Well, I won, duh. With my family in the audience, nobody else had a chance. They hand me the prize, a check for a thousand dollars. Totally wild. They want me to do my act again.

Sure beats babysitting.

DO, RE, ME, FA . . . AH, YOU KNOW. . .

Piano lessons . . . swimming lessons . . . dance class . . . tennis lessons . . . more piano lessons. If I have twenty-three minutes in a day to talk to my friends it's a miracle. I do a zillion things. Then it hit me, like, Hello, these were totally not my ideas. My mom would say, "Sweetie, I think you should take a dance class, ballet maybe, what do you think?" And I would go, "Well, yeah, why not, cool, sure." Well maybe not cool, but she always asked me while I was watching TV. So now I do all this stuff. I take, like, two days a week for this and two days a week for that. I tell her, "Mom, it like totally takes up all my time."

She goes, "I think you may be exaggerating, sweetie, it's only a few days a week."

I've met a lot of cool kids, anyway. Like in swimming class and my dance class. Oh, and my piano teacher, Mrs. Bramberg, she's played for, like, every major singer in practically every country in the world. She's even played in countries when wars were going on. So cool. So last week I had this piano recital. Don't you hate that word? It totally reeks. Recital, ug-a-lee! So I show up, nice gown, used to be Mom's, a really cool antique thing. Joyce, Mrs. Bramberg, she's got me all rehearsed with a classical thing from Brahms. Just a short thing, a lullaby, I worked on it for a couple of weeks. I couldn't even go to the mall. Okay . . . once I went to the movies.

I made one really lame mistake. I hit two keys with the same finger. But when I looked over at Mrs. Bramberg, she just smiled. After it was over, they tell me it was a Junior's Competition. Hit me in the face with a shovel! I mean, Mom and Joyce kept that part a secret. Well, I actually won! Can you believe it? I almost plotzed right then and there. They announce my name, I walk up to get the check, oh, and a ribbon with words on it. I can't believe it. I got me some mall money now.

THE ONLY THING WE DIDN'T DO
WAS KISS THE BLARNEY STONE

What a night! It was so cool. There were eight of us. We all go to school together and Katy's brother, Flynn, and his Irish folk-music band were playing at The Farmers' Market on Fridays for two weeks. The market is closed at night, but some of the food-a-terias stay open for the music. They set up a stage and mikes and bands come to play and grown-ups dance and stuff. One week it's salsa, and one week it's jazz, and for two weeks it was The Flying Flynn's Irish Folk Music. I never thought I'd like it so much. I got all the girls together to see if we wanted to dance there. No, not with guys. God, I'd die. But real Irish folk dancing. Okay, so three kids are black, one of us is Italian, two are Mexican, and the rest are Irish. Sounds like America to me.

I went to the library and got out books on Irish dancing and some tapes and we had of The Flynn's CDs, and we practiced. There was a lot of giggling, gossip, and falling into each other. It took around four days to finally get us all to start on the same foot. No adults, parents, friends, teachers, anybody, knew enough to help us. Believe me, I totally asked everybody. So we practiced and fell down, stepped on a lot of feet and giggled some more and all of a sudden it was working. The Flynn's play from six-thirty to nine-thirty, so we could still all get home on time. Anyway, we get there and we're totally ner-vousa-gigantica. They start playing, people are, like, trying to pick each other up, older people, sitting, tapping their feet and clapping and stuff. Finally Katy says, "Are we going to do this, or what?" So we get up on the edge of the dance floor, and when a song we practiced to started, we danced. We stood in a line and me and Katy got it going and then the other girls got into it. We were all dancing this totally Irish jig. We were giggling and it was hard to concentrate. But most of the time we were in step. Like coordinated, ya know? It was way cool.

The people in the back started standing up so they could see us better. The old people started clapping along. In the back, I see my dad stand up. I didn't even know he was there. I like totally gasped. He was smiling and clapping along and nudging the man next to him and pointing at me. Once he even waved to me. A little uncool, but nice. It was awesome. We only danced to that one song, but that night, that night was bitchin'!

I KNOW WHERE CARMEN SAN DIEGO IS

I thought I'd be too young, but I made it. Oh, yeah, Carmen San Diego is in a TV studio. I was there. I made it on to the show. Some girl got sick and they called me at the last minute. Dad drove me there so fast I thought I was going to have a heart attack.

The studio is really big, with a lot of lights. They gave me a nice jacket for the show, and when we played the quiz game, I was in the middle between some guy named Chris and this other girl. I had barrettes in my hair and braces. Well, I was totally young. We answered a lot of questions and for a while I was way behind. I think it was because I couldn't push that stupid button fast enough.

I did real well with the part right after Fact Finders. That's when I caught up. I even tied Chris, who was way smart. Then with the questions about 1936, I got Jesse Owens, Norway, Little League Baseball and The Leaning Tower of Pisa. After that, it was too close. The three of us were tied for a long time. Then on "Ultimate Date Boost" it got really tense. You really have to remember dates in sequence, but that was when I finally got the hang of that button.

The other girl got eliminated and there was just the two of us. Me and Chris. "Call me Christopher, please." This dude knew everything. Hey, but there I was, in the finals. All about the Olympics. Eight boxes in order of time. Miss one in the sequence and you turn it over to the other person. They miss and you go. He went first and missed. Then I missed about four dates in. Then he missed. Then I was sailing through it and I missed again. Now there was only four left and he missed on the third one. I went all the way to the two last dates and I messed up. I was *so* close.

Well, Christopher went and he aced it. Duh! I told you this dude was smart. Hey, but I came in second and I had a fabulous time. Got to keep the jacket and the people were very nice and we had snacks. The only thing I thought was weird was, like, some of the adult actors on the show all acted like they were re-tards. I think they think it's what kids want to see. Pa-leeeze! They were fine when they were off the air, but on the air, pure re-tard. Oh, yeah, Chris, er, Christopher is in his school play and he invited me. No barrettes, no braces.

NOT A TYPICAL DAY AT THE MALL

It was such a nice day. Saturday right after lunch. Me, my little sister, Henrietta, my friend Gigi and Gigi's mom, Mrs. Glottlieb are going shopping. So we're, like, headed to a mall she knows all the way on the other side of town. She's all, "You girls will love this place. Lots of nifty clothes." I'm thinking . . . Nifty? Will there be boys there? And if there are boys, and they live that far away, what's the point? Everybody is too young to drive and I can't see boys who are old enough to drive.

So we're there and walking around and boys are checking us out and we're pretending that we're not checking them out. I got three great outfits. Cute . . . a little dressy. Gigi came up empty. Her mother went retro and bought koo-lots. I'm like, "Eee-uuu!" So we eat and check and the boys eat and they check. When Gigi's mom went to the ladies' room, these dudes came over. They were so nervous. They gave us their numbers and we gave them ours. Like they're really going to call, right?

On the way home, Henrietta said she felt sick. Like she's going to hurl chunks. Mrs. Glottlieb panics. (*Beat*) Why? Like I know? Then she starts making little noises. Little, tiny, screaming noises. "Ee . . . eee . . . eee." Like that. What's up with that? Then I get it. She's not upset because of Henrietta, something is happening to *her*. All of a sudden her eyes get totally weird and roll up in her head and her head hits the steering wheel. Bang! I didn't know what to think.

Henrietta and Gigi start screaming, and I reached over and grabbed the steering wheel, but Mrs. Glotlieb is all over it. I push her back and try to slide over to my left a little and of course her foot is still on the gas. Now we're going faster. "Gigi, hold your mother out of the way!" This I had to say, like, four times before she gets it. Like, duh, hello! Come on already, it's an emergency. Get into some non-fiction here, babe. So she finally pulls her mom back and the car is playing snake all over the road. I got her size-nine, double-E foot off the gas and the car slowed down and then I pushed on the brake, just easy like, and turned the wheel so we got off the road. Seemed like it took a million years. The car finally stops. I grabbed Gigi's cell phone and called 911. Meanwhile, Henrietta's now barfing out the window and Gigi's a mess. And Mrs. Glotlieb is making different noises now. "Oh, oh, oh my God, oh no. What's happening? Call a doctor." Stuff like that. After a few minutes the ambulance gets there and they put her in it. Since I also called my dad, he showed up as the ambulance was about to pull away. The ambulance driver told dad what I'd done and they're all calling me a heroine. As if!

Mrs. Glotlieb and Henrietta had just eaten something gross. She wants to sue the mall . . . blah, blah, blah. Those boys? They never called. Why do they bother to take the number? Brain-dead jerks. Except for the one in the blue sweater. Maybe I'll call him.

YOU ALWAYS WIND UP BACK AT SCHOOL

Hi, where I come from is really, like, no more. Gone. Three years ago we were fine. Everything was cool. My family wasn't dysfunctional. When we sat down to dinner nobody yelled or was mean. Even my kid brother and sister, who are pains, weren't too flipped out. Then, the rains started and wouldn't stop. They even closed the schools. A day later the river, near us, overflowed its banks, overflowed the flood basins, and totally flooded the town. Thing is, it came way fast. We all knew about it, it's all anybody talked about. Then it was like insta-flood. In less than a few hours our whole house was under water, totally. Dad and Mom grabbed what they could and tried to move it to the upstairs. Freddie and Annabelle, my sibs, were grabbing toys. Can't let the video games get wet. Well, we're upstairs listening to the portable radio and hoping the batteries last and waiting for someone to rescue us. Nobody came. We needed a boat or something.

The rain stopped but the water kept getting higher. Nobody knew what to do. Then I looked up the hill and noticed the Strassner's garage. I know they have a boat and they were away on business. So, because I'm a strong swimmer—I'm on the swimming team at school—I just crawled out on the porch roof. Before my family knew what was going on, I was gone. I dove into the water and swam over to the Strassner's garage. When I got there I couldn't figure out how to open the garage door from the outside. Too much water. I swam around to the side, and with a piece of floating wood, I totally broke the window. I got in and stood on the roof of their car and pressed the button. Nothing happened. No electricity. I got it open by hand and all the water flooded in and knocked me backward. I felt pretty stupid. But the flooding loosened the boat! I got it in position and rowed it out of the garage and right over to my house.

The family was all on the porch roof watching and waiting and my dad jumped in and helped get the boat to the roof. They all got in, but before we could go half a block, the rescue team came and got us to safety. You know where that was? My school. What a day. All my buds were there and everybody was safe. Plus we didn't have any classes.

IT SEEMED LIKE THE RIGHT THING TO DO

Hello. Please pardon me if I don't speak your language too well. My sister and me came to America only a short time ago. I am from Central America and I cannot tell you the country, because they are still looking for us. I think. They think we will tell them where our mother and father are hiding. They, we, are called revolutionaries and the federal troops want them.

You see, my sister, Juanita, took me to the beach, in our country, one day. We had a nice time. No one was shooting at us, or chasing us, or breaking in to our house trying to find Mama and Papa. We were just swimming and eating and laughing and splashing. Then we saw them! Up on the ridge behind the beach. Trucks and jeeps with lots of federal soldiers. We were the only ones there, so we knew they were looking for us. My sister, she's older than I am, grabbed a big, plastic trash bag and stuffed our clothes in it and tied it closed very tight and then wrapped it around her waist. She grabbed my hand and ran into the water. I was so afraid. She said, "Swim out to that floating wood past the breakers!" So I did. We did. The soldiers drove onto the beach and fired a few shots at us, but we were too far away and the sea did not cooperated with them, it kept moving up and down. We grabbed the wood and held on and drifted. I found out later that we were in the water for eleven hours. We drifted north with the current, and it's a good thing tropical water is warm. The sharks and jellyfish like it, too.

I looked like a prune when I got out. The wood landed us across the border in another country. I can't tell you that country either—we were there illegally. An old fisherman found us and brought us in his truck to a church. The people from the church took us to the International Red Cross. They took us to Amnesty International. Amnesty International found relatives of ours here in the United States. Right here in this city. El Norte, where everyone is free.

Our relatives are very nice. We are free here. Thank God for America. Thank God for so many things, including the death of the Macarena. We tried to contact our parents for almost two years, and one week ago we talked to them on the phone. I asked them if they were mad because we ran away. They said, "Oh, no, you and Juanita were very brave. They would have killed you. It's over now, me and your mother will get out soon and be with you soon! I promise you, we will be together, always."

Guess what? They come tomorrow! We are all going to meet them at the airport. You people are lucky to live in this country your whole life.

WHAT'S THE BIG DEAL? FIND SOME DIRT, SEEDS AND WATER.

Our apartment building is at the end of the block. Next to it is this empty lot somebody was going to build on a couple of years ago, and didn't. It was all weeds and junk people threw there. A total mess. Well, a few wild flowers came up, too.

My dad was always saying, "It's a shame that someone doesn't do something constructive with that land. What an eyesore." Well, I did. One Saturday, I went, with a rake, and cleared out a bunch of weeds and made a spot to plant things. I was going to plant flowers, then I thought food would be better. I took my allowance and brought tomatoes, carrots, squash . . . stuff like that. The soil there must be very rich, because with just some watering, all these things grew. When I picked the first tomato, and brought it home, Mom and Dad got very excited. "Fresh vegetables from the garden, wow!" So I cleared a little more space and planted more. Well, two years of this and people in the neighborhood are calling me "Garden Girl," and I tell them to help themselves. Ya know why? Because it's impossible for one family to eat all this stuff. You really get a lot for a little. A whole lot.

Then I had another idea. Three blocks from my house, on the way to school, some homeless people have been staying under an overpass. Well, I thought, this is a good place to bring all the extra food. So one Sunday morning, while they were still asleep, me, Marty, Vicki, and Cookie took some to them and left it so they would find it when they woke up. Then we started doing it a couple of mornings a week. Then one of them saw us and thanked us. Then he said, "Where are you getting this from?" I told them that I grew it. Then I said, "You can have all you like if you'll help weed and water and watch over it so it doesn't get vandalized. Some of them said they would, and they did. They still do. Yesterday Dad said that the property was sold and that an apartment building is going to go up there. Well . . . it was great while it lasted.

JUST SIGN IT

I just don't get some of my closest friends. I've known these kids almost all my life and have gone through school with them, and I thought I really knew them.

I'll tell you what's up. Last semester, a new girl, Regina, came into our class. She had this big clunky device stuck in her ear, 'cause she's deaf. So I introduce myself. I had to talk real slow to her. It was like walking through oatmeal. When I looked for Regina after school, she wasn't there because a special bus picks her up and takes her to a special school where she learns I-don't-know-what. Deaf stuff, I guess. When I talked to my buds about including her in stuff, I noticed they all had other things to do. Molly called Regina a geek and didn't want to be seen with her. The other girls made fun of her. Not to her face, behind her back. They made faces and gestures when she wasn't looking, like this. Real funny unless you're the one they're making fun of.

I noticed Regina getting out of her car one morning and saying goodbye to her mom using sing language. That was so cool. Like a secret code. How often does that come up? So I asked Regina to teach it to me.

We worked on it every day at lunch. I got pretty good at it after a while. Now we can talk in class when the teacher's back is turned and we never get caught. When Molly and the others complained they felt left out, I told them, "Tough tidepools, girls!"

Then I got up in an assembly and signed a talk on the Signing of the Magna Carta. Regina loved my little surprise and so did the assembly. Then everybody wanted to know how to sign, even Molly. Well, not everybody, but a lot of kids. So me and Regina teach them at lunch time. Now there are almost forty of us who can sign and the teachers have no idea what's up with us.

It's cool to know a second language.

I KNOW, I KNOW . . . THAT'S HOW I AM

It's, like, I was born with this ESP. I know things. Without calling the Psychic Hotline. Like I knew my mom was going to have my baby sister before she did. Like one day while I was cramming for a math test, I get this feeling, I get this flash. Mom is pregnant! I say to her, "Mom, do you have some special 411 you want to share?"

She says, "What do you mean?" Mom knows me by now. "What's on that extra-terrestrial mind of yours?"

So, I go, "Well I think that we'll be having a visitor."

She says, "If you're talking about your Uncle Lenny and aunt Josephine coming for dinner, it's not news."

"No, another kind of visitor, you want to know about it, or what?"

She looked at me strange. "Now what? You been looking into that crystal ball of yours again?"

I said, "Well, before I tell you, you'd better run upstairs and unplug your curling iron so we don't have a fire."

"My curling iron! Oh, no!" She runs for the stairs and I keep right on talking.

I yelled up the stairs, "You're going to have a baby! Want to know the sex?" Behind me I heard something drop. I turned around and there was Dad with just a saucer in his hand. The cup is history. Mom comes down the steps with her curling iron.

"What did you say?"

"You're pregnant, I see a little girl." They were stunned. Then they hugged.

Mom said, "Okay, I'll go find out for sure today. Are you sure?"

"Yep," was all I said. More hugging.

(*Suddenly holding her head, thinking*) Hmm . . . my sister's name is going to be . . . Stephanie. I guess I'd better go and tell them. Oh, by the way, I aced that math test.

PUT YOUR MIND WHERE YOUR MOUTH IS

I'm really excited to be here. If you would have seen me one year ago—a little more than a year ago—I wouldn't be here today. Because I used to be that much overweight. I was a different person.

Mom said, "It's baby fat, you'll lose it as your body matures." Like when? I'm suppose to be Orca's double until my body matures? Yeah, right! Not cool.

A week after what my mom said, I signed up for this nutrition-cooking-class thing at school. It's after school and a volunteer runs it. This volunteer, Mrs. Birch, she taught us how to pick the right foods. She says, over and over, "Nobody your age needs to be on a diet if you will just eat right in the first place."

Eating right meant eating lots of fruits and vegetables. Did you know that vegetables are mostly water? Rice, pasta, and potatoes are all really good for you if you don't put a whole bunch of fat junk on them. You should also cut way back on your fat intake.

Then we started learning how to cook whole meals with hardly any meat in them. Sooo delicious. Now I cook fish instead of Mom's fish sticks. Processed food is the worst. I can cook chicken a bunch of different ways. And tofu, too. Tofu is like magic. It sucks up the flavor of whatever is around it.

We never fried anything in class, so I never learned how. We only used extra-virgin olive oil on things. It's better that way. I know all about the food pyramid, too.

Mrs. Birch told us that our attitude and moods when we eat have a lot to do with things. In the late afternoons, I used to be dying for a junk-food snack: a candy bar or a pop tart, stuff like that. Instead of eating this junk, she told us to make a cup of this fat-free, Chef Piero's Gourmet Chicken Base. You drink it like a broth and it suppresses your hunger and it's good for you. It's a restaurant trick. Her uncle is Chef Piero. Then she said, "Food is necessary and a pleasure, and when you cook for someone, it's a gesture of love."

Anyhow, that's all I wanted to say, except that I love Mrs. Birch, and I love the way I look. Except for my hair. That's next.

BOYS

THEY CALL ME A HERO,
BUT IT'S JUST COMMON SENSE TO ME

It all started a few weeks ago. Actually, it all started years ago, but that was before I knew what was up.

My parents wanted to get a divorce. Really tough on my kid brother and sister. Me, I'm older so I can handle this stuff a little easier. A lot of my homies have divorced parents, so we talk about it a lot.

My mom is the one who started the whole thing. My bedroom wall is between me and my folks so, duh, it was really easy to hear the fighting. Real loud. You could have heard them on the moon. Like, man, it really reeked. Every night was screaming and yelling and more yelling. Somehow, I don't know, it didn't seem real.

One night my father yelled at her, "You're just like your mother!" This got me to thinking. My mother's mother divorced my mother's father, so maybe she was just, like, following in her footsteps. Maybe like a role-model thing. So one night, when me and Mom were eating dinner and Dad and my little brother and sister were out buying me a "surprise" birthday cake, I asked Mom if maybe, like, she was just doing what her mother did. She almost dropped a plate. Then she said, "You're too young to know what's going on, keep your mouth shut and your nose out of my business!" Like a divorce isn't the business of the whole family. Right, give me a break. But I knew I was on to something. She'd never talked to me like that before.

That night I was in my room, doing my homework, but really wanting to kick it, and instead of hearing yelling and fighting I hear quiet talking. I couldn't make out what they were saying because they weren't yelling. Next day the house is, like, normal. My brother is being a pain, my sister is off in never-never land, just the usual stuff. Next night, again no yelling. 'Sup with that?

About a week goes by and when we are all actually sitting down to dinner together, my dad says, "Well, family, your mother and I have some interesting news. We've decided to stay together and get some counseling." Then he reached over and touched her hand. Then Mom said, "We owe a lot of this decision to Frank, because something he said to me is what started this thing in motion. Your dad and I have been sorting through this since he mentioned my mother to me and what she did." Like, wow, man, just like, way wow!

At first I thought I was hallucinating, or whacked out on the carrots, or, I don't know what. Then there was all the hugging and kissing and laughing and joking like it used to be. Hey, ya know, I was just trying to help. Like I said before, a divorce would have been real hard on my little brother and sister.

WHEN IS IT EVER ENOUGH?

Ever meet a dude, or dudette, that to them nothing is ever enough? Whatever you do, or do for them, they're never satisfied? To my dad, I do okay. But he lives in another state. I only see him every once in a while. My mom is the one I can never satisfy. Her and my cousin Artie. If I do my homework and she checks and it's cool, she asks me, "Did you do anything for extra credit?" And Artie is all, like, "If you go to the game, can I come?" After, he won't even thank you.

One day I find a bird on the sidewalk and it's flapping around like it totally can't fly. There was this big old cat staring at it, so I took it home. I put it in an old milk crate and put a screen over it. But then I didn't know what to do for it. So I got a bird book from the library and looked up some stuff. It said what the bird was called and what it ate and where it liked to live and a lot of good stuff. Turns out it's from the jungle in Central America. I got the things it liked to eat and put it in a warm place. Then I noticed what was wrong. A bone, a tiny little bone on its wing was sticking out. Well, I'm, like, not a vet, or anything, but what the heck. I lift the bird and gently, like a whisper, I put the bone back in place. Then I put a little scotch tape around it so it wouldn't pop out again. My mom said, "How long is that dirty thing going to be here?" I didn't know. Artie said, "Oh you never know nuffin!" I just walked away.

A couple of weeks passed and I took the screen off the milk crate. The bird just sat there. All green and yellow and blue and sitting. The next morning I check the grate and the bird is gone! Window open, bird gone. I looked out and it was sitting in our tree. Then, just like that, it flew away. I told Mom and everybody, but nobody cared. Then four days later it was sitting on my window sill. Mom said, "Is that dirty thing back again?" It flew away and I never saw it again. I guess it came back to say, "See ya." Or maybe, "Thanks." Who knows?

Now I'm thinking maybe I could be a vet when I grow up.

THE BIZ THERE'S NO BIZ LIKE

Hi, my name is Kirk and I can now officially call myself an Actor. I got paid to act, so I am a professional actor.

My neighbor has a show for children on Sundays. The theater is only about ten minutes from here by car. My parents took me to see it three or four times when I was little. It's the kind of show where they let the kids come on stage and do stuff. I used to be on the stage as much as I was in my seat. Then, one Sunday, about two hours before the show, my neighbor called my mom—I was at her house for that week—and he asks her if he could use me in the show. She asked me and I said, "Yesss!" Well, he picked me up and gave me a show T-shirt to wear, and told me what he wanted me to do in the show.

At the theater there was just me and him and another grown-up actor. They started to rehearse the stuff with me I was going to do in the show. I practically knew the whole show by heart anyway. I go where they tell me and say what I'm supposed to say in the show. Then it comes time for the improvisation. An improvisation is you just make it up as you go along. They didn't think I could handle that, so they said, "Look, if you think of something, jump in; if not, we'll handle it. Remember, there are no mistakes, only opportunities to get better."

So the people showed up and paid their money and sat down and we started. I did everything they said and when the improv came around, I knew I could do it. Did you ever just feel like you could do something? So they're doing this improvisation about saving Hansel and Gretel and I walked on stage and started talking like Batman. I was Batman rescuing Hansel and Gretel from The Old Witch. It was so cool, everybody clapped. After the show I got my share of the money from the audience. Seven dollars. Money for acting. I *told* you I was a pro.

I HOPE YOU LIKE IT, I MADE IT

I have this friend . . . well, he's really my dad's friend. They're close buds from a long time ago. I mean long ago, like B.C. You know, Before Cable. Dad's friend, his name is Piero, he owns a restaurant near here. He owned it before I was born. Kinda B.M.—Before Me.

My class at school was going on this big trip to Muggsie's Miracle Night of Mayhem and Mystery. It's really cool, also totally expensive. But you have to pay for the trip all by yourself. Well I didn't have any money, so I had to earn it. I tried asking people if I could deliver stuff, rake leaves, yard work, wash their cars—anything. They just totally said no, they don't need any help. I was major bummed out.

I was with my dad when he stopped at Piero's to get some supper to go. I asked Piero if he needed any help around the restaurant. Like he was going to hire a kid, right. I was thinking maybe busing tables, washing dishes, something like that. He goes, "Yes, I could use a little help in the kitchen." Then I saw him wink at my father. So he takes me into the kitchen and starts showing me how to cut onions, dice them really, without crying. Then he showed me how to bone a duck. Totally awesome. Bone a duck. That means take out all the bones and leave the duck in one piece. It was, well, I thought it would be way hard, but the way he showed me made it seem easier. Then he says, "You start tomorrow, after school, from four to nine, Wednesday through Saturday. Then he tells me what the job pays. Knocked me out.

I went to work and did what his chef told me to do. I learned a lot about cooking. One problem was when it came time to buy the tickets for Muggsie's Miracle Night of Mayhem and Magic, I couldn't go. Piero was catering a big wedding reception and asked if I wanted to make some extra money. Tough call? Not even. I went to work. Muggsie's will always be there. I'm an apprentice.

NOTHING SPECIAL . . . JUST CAMP

Hi, last year my dad sent me to camp. It was a basketball camp coached by some coach who coaches at a college near here. I'm pretty good and I like to play. Got me a hoop over my garage door. I even put up a light so I can practice at night. This was a good thing, because I got good enough to make my school team. Basketball camp was okay, but all you do is play ball and go to basketball clinics every day. I mean, come on, even though you're into basketball, this can get old real fast.

This year my parents sent me to a camp in the mountains. Wow! Man, what a difference. There were, like, crafts . . . not cool. But we played baseball, and Frisbee football . . . that was cool. And there were girls there. This was a little awkward at first, but then, after a while, it got non-awkward, totally cool.

One night we had this dance, okay? Well, it didn't start off too well because all the guys stood at one end of the room and all the girls stood at the other. This went on for a while until the girls got tired of waiting for someone to ask them to dance, so they started dancing with each other. Finally, I thought, Hey, this is stupid. So, I asked Marie Davis to dance. It was like I'd committed murder, or something. Everybody totally stopped and watched. She started to get embarrassed and said, "Why are they all looking at us?" Then I said, I don't even know where it came from, I said, "Because you're really cute and a cool dancer." Well she smiled this great big smile and she hugged me. Then the guys got real stupid. They started making "ooooo" noises. Sounded like cows. "Ooooooo! ooooo!"

Finally the other girls got fed up with waiting around and started asking . . . no, not exactly asking . . . more like dragging the guys onto the dance floor. The rap was cool. The rock was cool. The lights sparkled. People were laughing and talking and singing along with the music while they were dancing. Like, duh! A real party! You don't get this at basketball camp.

JUST A LINE ON A GRAPH

It was supposed to be detention for me because I was supposed to have been talking. Bull. Not true. Doesn't matter, 'cause as punishment I got put in a Graphic Arts course for one period where a bunch of jerks were drawing on paper that was full of lines. Hey, if you're going to draw something, shouldn't the paper be, like . . . empty? But these kids had paper with lines. Give me a break. When I mention this to the teacher, Mr. Johnson, he says, "As long as you are in this class, you'll do what we're doing." Okay by me. I wasn't about to get into more trouble.

So they're all drawing and I'm just totally sitting. I can't draw because I can't handle all the lines. I like to draw. I even paint, sometimes. This? This was way weird. So I sit, pencil ready, but nothing comes to me. Mr. Johnson comes by and says, "Having trouble?"

I say, "Yeah, well, kinda. The lines are in the way so I can't draw."

Then he sits down and gives me that old can't-is-a-very-limiting-word story. "Let me see if I can help," he says. Then he picks up my hand with the pencil in it and says, "If you see the lines as a problem, they'll be a problem. But, if you see the lines as a help, they'll be a help. Got it?"

I go, "No." Then he starts making a line. Then something, like, must have totally connected in my head because alluva sudden I saw what he meant. He took his hand off mine and I started to draw. A horse, a running horse, just from going from line to line. Almost like connect-the-dots, only the dots were in my mind. Mr. Johnson liked the drawing enough to hang it up with a couple of the others. He asked me if I wanted to take his class, but I didn't have room on my schedule. So he gave me some graph paper and I draw at home now. Only, like now, the pictures aren't of horses, they're pictures of things I only used to be able to see in my mind.

NOTHING BUT VERY COLD, HARD WATER,
EVERYWHERE

"H-e-y Billy! H-e-y Billy!"

When I finally looked out the window Juan was standing in the middle of the sidewalk, holding ice skates and yelling his head off. Like, dead Laplanders could hear him. Like he never heard of doorbells, right? "Didn't you hear me, man? Come on, we're heading for the rink!" I thought, Aw no, not ice skating. The last time I went ice skating I really reeked. My ankles hurt, I fell all the time, girls were laughing at me and making gestures with their hands over their mouths, looking at me like I was El Spazzo. I hated it.

Ice skating is not my whatever. I like warm days, baseball, swimming, like that. I'm a warm-weather guy. Hey, the way I see it, hot is cool. Well, cool is also hot. But, cold is not cool.

And the next-to-last time I went skating, I fell down and a girl materialized next to me and helped me up. I was really embarrassed. But she was okay. Her name was, is, Annette and she had, has, dark hair and she was . . . nice. She is nice. She gave me some pointers. She told me how to carry my weight and how to lean forward and let the skates glide. She said I was too much in my head and not enough in my "trust zone." Whatever that is. Then she took my arm and guided me around the ice. She went real slow and talked to me in a voice that sounded like a soft, slow song. The kind you really want to hear the words to. So we skate and she talks and I say nothing, like king dork. We were kickin' it fine until Jaun, Herman and Big Jar showed up. His name is Jared, but he looks like a big jar and he walks like one.

They start in yelling and bugging us and distracting us and when I grabbed the side rail Annette got totalled and went down hard. They were all laughing and I told 'em to shut up. Lame-os. I helped Annette up and started to apologize for my friends, but she just skated away. I skated around looking for her, but she'd disappeared. Bummer.

"Hey Billy, you coming, or what?"

"Oh, yeah, Juan. No, man, I don't feel like it today."

"Oh yeah?" He goes, "I heard that that girl Annette is gonna be there today.

Hey, was I outta here. Down the stairs and out the door. Hey, ice skating is good for physical fitness.

OKAY, HE'S A GUY, BUT HE KNEW WHAT TO DO

I've have this friend named Andre. He lives in the building next to mine. He's a cool dude. And a great athlete: football, baseball, basketball, track. Like this dude has all-city qualifications. The thing is, he's always looking to earn a few bucks because he comes from a single-parent family and his dad is an actor and actors don't work steady. Anyway, we're just kickin' one Saturday, tossing a football around, and Andre says to me, "Who moved in next door to you?"

I say, "Some lady with a baby. Just got divorced."

He says, "Think they need a babysitter?" A babysitter? Whoa!

"First off, no I don't. Second, you might be too young. Third, you're not a girl and they usually hire girls to babysit."

He says, "Go deep . . . no, really long . . . I'll ask her anyway." Then he throws me a pass that was a perfect strike. Awesome.

A few days later, I drop by his crib to see if he wants to go to the movies. He tells me he has the money because he made it babysitting for my new neighbor. But there was some trouble because the mother didn't come home at ten o'clock, like she said, and the baby started acting real weird around eleven. So I'm, like, "What weird, what'd you do?" He told me he fed the baby, burped it, changed its diaper and then called his dad. His dad told him he did good but hit the ceiling when he found out the mother didn't get back on time. Total bummer. Then Andre found a pack of matches with the name of this bar on it. He called the number on the matches and asked for the woman. This was like at midnight or one A.M. The woman was at that bar. He told her it was way past his bedtime, that he had school the next day and that she better get home, now. She did. Turned out she has the drinking disease. I hope she gets some help. It's not right to leave a kid in charge of an infant, like that. But that Andre, he was so cool under pressure. Handled it like an adult. What a dude.

ON YOUR MARKS. GET SET. BANG.
RUN LIKE THE WIND.

First off, I've always been fast. Ya know, running, like. I guess I'm athletic. When I was about four, my parents called me "The Blur."

Anyway, one day I'm at school and just kickin' back with my homies on the athletic field when the track team comes out to practice. They're all jumping around and stretching, so I walk over to see what's happening.

As I got near the track, some of them were lining up for a practice run of the hundred meter dash. I stand off the track to one side and the coach goes, "On your marks . . . get set . . . go!" They go. Boom! Like out of a cannon, or something. So I go, too. Why not? No problem. I'm only running on the infield dirt. Next thing I know I'm passing them. I mean like really flying. One guy tries to catch up to me and I blew him away. When I get to the finish line and look back they're still, like, halfway back. And these dorks are all in running shoes and shorts and I'm wearing my good shoes and new baggies. I figure the coach is going to go off on me for showing up his team. He goes, "Hey, what's your name?"

"Andre," I tell him.

"You're pretty fast, you know that? You wanna to join the track team?" I didn't know what to say. "Think about it," he said. "You could win a lotta meets. How about it?" So I said okay.

After school I went by the coach's office and signed up. My parents signed the consent form and I had a physical. Then I started running. The coach taught me how to start and about body positioning and stuff and the next thing I know we're at a track meet. The dudes and babes on my team are all cool and you get to go to other schools and other schools come to us. I didn't think it would be this much fun.

Oh, yeah, I ran in the city finals and won. They gave me a medal and a trophy and my dad kept telling anybody, "That's my son, he's all-city!" Alluva sudden everyone knew who I was. They wrote me up in the newspapers. I was even interviewed on TV once.

It's great being "The Blur."

NOT RE-ACTING? TRY IT, YOU'LL LIKE IT.

At first it was bad, not good-bad, bad-bad. I couldn't get along with anybody. It was like . . . like I had a disease. Then one day I'm walking home past old man Biondi's place; a great old man, like, a half-million years old who lives by himself at the end of our street. He lets me pick apples off his trees. So, I'm going home and I hear a voice. Really spooky. "You look like you've got the troubles of the world on your shoulders, young man."

I turn around and he's there where he wasn't just a moment before. He appears poof, like a genie. I say hello and we start talking and pretty soon we're sitting on his front steps and he's telling me stuff I never heard of. Like, we're made up of two parts, the ego and the self. That my ego is my enemy and does all of this bad stuff to me and my Self. He says, "Spell it with a capital S because it's what connects you to the universe." So he tells me how I make up stuff in my head, and that if I stop reacting to what people say and just be my Self, with a capital S, that I can look at life like it's a movie and not something I gotta fight against, or win over, or junk like that. It took me a while, but I finally got what he meant. Then he says to try to figure out where the person, who is talking, is coming from. "Don't just react. Don't try to get them to like you, either. A waste of time." We talked all afternoon.

When I got home, Mom was there. What a surprise. She's like all yelling and asking where I've been so long and why I'm coming home at this hour. So I tried what Mr. Biondi said, to figure out what was up with her. I think, She's worried about me and feeling a little guilty because she can't give me more attention. So I just gave her a hug. "It's okay, Mom, you seem a little stressed out, I was just hanging with Mr. Biondi. You look tired, can I get you some cranberry juice?" She's like stunned. She hugs me back and tells me she'd love some juice and that she *is* tired; tired and worried, and over-worked and that raising four kids by herself isn't easy.

I got the juice and she gave me another hug. A person could get used to this hugging stuff. Then my older brother came in with his bud, Mark the dork, and started picking on me. I just stepped back and said, "Hi, I hope your team won. I hope you struck out their whole stupid team."

He goes, "I did okay."

Then I go, "Hi Mark, 'sup?"

He picked his nose and said, "Shut up, twerp."

I said, "They didn't let you play again, huh? Bummer. Well when they see how good you're getting, you'll be starting every game. It must get lonely for you."

He goes, "I'm not lonely. Shut up, you weirdo!" Then he runs out of the house. So much for him. Then that night he called to apologize. The dork, apologizing?

This non-reacting stuff is pretty cool.

I THINK I FOUND A WAY TO MAKE SOME MONEY

A couple of years ago, I broke this ankle. See? This left one. It was funny how it happened. I enjoy reading, okay? So I was standing at a bus stop reading a Steven King novel. I was so totally into the book that I didn't realize the bus was practically on top of me. It startled me and I jumped back. Next thing I know my heel catches the edge of the cement thing that holds up the bus bench. My ankle not only breaks, it shatters. I didn't realize it at first, but when I stepped on my left foot, I couldn't feel the ground. They had to call an ambulance.

I was laid up for a long time. Lots of time for reading. Also my best friend, Latrell, gave me a bunch of tape cassettes to listen to. A few days later, while I'm listening to one of his tapes, the tape jams and then breaks. Bummer. It was a cool sound and I wanted to hear it so I took the cassette out of the Walkman and it's spaghetti. So I hobble to the kitchen and find dad's tool kit . I take a tiny screwdriver out and very carefully open the cassette. I get a little piece of clear scotch tape, repair the break, put the cassette together and it worked fine. My brother sees what I did and says, "Can you fix one of my tapes, too?" I didn't know, but I had a lot of time to try, so I said I'd a take a look at it. Well, I fiddled with the tape all afternoon but I got it fixed. Then I thought, Hey, maybe I'm on to something here.

I let the word out that I could fix any cassette. I didn't know that I could, but I'd sure give it a shot. A few people brought broken cassettes around and I actually fixed them. Then I started charging them for materials. Then I added a small labor charge, like a buck or two. They paid it gladly. As you can see, my ankle is fine now. (*He does a little dance step*) And I'm still fixing broken cassettes. I going to print up flyers and hand them out. This is turning into a good thing for me. Maybe you should think about getting into something. But if you're going to start a business, I don't recommend that you break an ankle, or anything else.

SUNDAY MORNING IN THE RAIN

Let's see, I was, like, seven at the time and it was Sunday morning. When I say Sunday morning, I mean, like seven-thirty or eight o'clock. And I'm all dressed up for church, okay? We used to go at nine o'clock and you had to be on time. My parents were manic about it. Anyway, I got this suit on and a hat, with a brim that looked like it belonged to an old man in the nineteen forties, or something. I mean if it looked like Indiana Jones' hat, or something, maybe I wouldn't have wanted to B and D. You know— barf and die. Here I am seven years old and I'm wearing a shirt and tie and this hat. As if!

Okay, and here I am on top of this garage roof, okay? It had a pointy, slanted roof and I was in the middle. And I was up there to jump from one roof to another. Way dangerous. But, ya see, the day before, I was with these older dudes from the 'hood and they jumped across real easy. They just stood back, and then they ran up and just jumped across every time. No prob. They told me to try it but I was too scared to jump. I froze. They called me "coward" and "baby" and a bunch of other junk and I told them I had to split and went home. I was outta there warp-speed. They didn't see me crying. But all that night it really bothered me. I don't remember what I watched on TV, or ate, or anything.

Next morning, I'm up early. I ate, put on the dorky church clothes and headed for the door. My mom says, "Put your hat on, it's raining." G and C—groan and curse. I go to the garage and climb up the drainpipe, which was slippery because it was drizzling. And it was real windy and the stupid hat blows off. I get to the top and make my way to the highest point. You know, where the big dudes jumped over. I must have stood there for, I don't know, forever. I was a statue, man, staring at the ground way down there. I wanted to, didn't want to. Finally I knew I had to leave or jump because it was pretty close to Church time. So I backed up. The rain was falling harder by then. I guess I ran and, like, jumped. I don't remember. All I know was that I was on the other roof. I was, like, stunned. Just then my father came around the corner looking for me. He sees me on the roof in my suit and yells for me to get down. I came to my senses real fast. I shimmied down another drainpipe and he says, "What were you doing up there, it's raining, where's your hat?"

I just shrugged, looked around, saw my hat, and put the stupid thing on my head. The rest of the day was a blur 'cause all I could think of was that jump. That jump, that jump was cool. Oh, yeah, I, like . . . later I accidentally lost the hat.

ORGANIZATION IS THE NAME OF THE GAME

"Let's get organized!" This is my mom's favorite expression. And when she says it, she means it. She makes the plans, does the organizing, and we do all the work. Except for my dad, who is always too busy at the right time.

My French class teacher, Mr. La Pinhead, said that this year the French class was going to start an annual French Class Picnic. Then he asked for volunteers to help organize the thing. I hear the word "organized" so much I raised my hand.

So, he gives me a date—April 17th—and says that a picnic spot near the lake would be perfect. That's it, a date and a site. Well, excuse *moi*! So I call my friend Dave. His father has a van. A big one. Then I called Mr. Ripplinger because he has a big van, too. Then I made up a list of stuff to bring: charcoal and paper plates and plastic cups and a tent and a surprise dish, too. The tent was my idea. I thought a little shelter might come in handy. Then I figured out who does what, and when they do it. Who does the picking up, who does the cleaning up. I thought it might be fun if the kids brought the food and the parents helped with the barbecue and then cleaned up. I fired up my computer and got it all written down and printed it out and made copies.

Well, Saturday the 17th comes and I'm on the phone from seven o'clock in the morning making sure everything goes right. Then I remember I didn't have a dish to bring. I organized everything but me. "Mom, what am I going to make?"

"Baby, I'm on clean up duty, I don't care what you make."

Nice answer, Mom. Sixteen turkey sandwiches later we're on our way. We got to the picnic site, and everybody had done what they were supposed to do. Perfect. Then, of course, it started to rain. Remember the tent? A million people squeezed into a small tent eating and singing, in French, in the rain. What a blast! I got an "A."

IT'S NOT THE DEBATING TEAM

Any ideas you have about what the Oration Team does are probably not complete. I'm not saying you're totally out of whack but. . . .

We are the Oration Team. Mr. Lawrence got it started, and for a while I was, like, well . . . I was the only one on the team. It took a while and trips to other schools to get other kids interested but, eventually, we got it moving. Now there are five of us and we're looking pretty good.

Just so you don't misunderstand, we only debate about ten percent of the time. Usually we give talks, orate on a subject. Who picks the subjects? I don't know. Some computer geek with a dweeb override. Like once we had this subject "The Plight of the Family Farmer." We all live in a big city. I've never even met a farmer. But here we are doing research, trying to find out the 411 on family farmers. We hardly found anything, so we made it all up. I thought nobody else would be able to find anything either. When the team met, I got Sarah and Jim to pretend that they were farmers and Susan and Asad to pretend that they represented a big farming company. Then, after a while, with each one making up stuff they thought sounded right, we made some notes and came up with the beginning of an oration. We had no idea if we were totally wrong or right or whatever.

So comes the night of the orations, and it was at our school. My dad never comes to school stuff. First, he's too busy, and second, I don't play on the basketball team like my brother. But, I peaked out and saw him and my mom and I got totally nervous. So we begin, and I'm up third. Jim does fine, and Asad, even with his accent, is making big points with what the big farming companies do for us: like holding prices down, employing a lot of people, and like that.

When I get up, my mouth is dry. I start talking, er, orating. First I talk about family values; a meaningless phrase that politicians throw around when they can't think of what to say. I mention kids getting up early and doing chores before they go to school, and how it builds character, and creates positive work habits for an adult life. I still don't know where I got this stuff from, but it came out. I finished before I knew it was over.

There was this deadly pause and I was totally freaked. Then they started to clap, and my teammates swarmed over me. Everybody liked it. Dad was on has feet clapping and Mom might have been crying a little. Off on the side, almost out of sight, Mr. Lawrence was doing a little dance.

So, if you want to find out about stuff, just ask the Oration Team. We may not know what we're talking about, but we'll sure sound like we do.

STAY TUNED FOR THE NEWS

I didn't mean for it to be such a big deal. Like, I only wanted to have some fun with the new video equipment at school. It's supposed to be there for everybody. Trouble is, there wasn't anybody who knew how to run it or teach a course in it, or anything. Hello!

So I wandered into the room where they keep the stuff. Beautiful video cameras, two of them. Monitors, control panels. Totally cool. I'm looking at this stuff and my bud, Terryl, comes in. He's pretty cool. He's into a lot of the stuff I'm into and he's a little shy. I can hang with that. He asks me what I'm doing and what happens if we get caught. Get caught? Get real. Then he finds a big instruction manual. When we go through it, we realize we need Miriam. She's good at all this figuring-stuff-out stuff.

She came, and the three of us were there till six-thirty, but we got the system up and running. Just when we turned the cameras on and started messin' around, Mr. Clifton comes in. Old Lonesome George, we call him because he's got nobody and nothing to go home to—that's why he was there so late. He blew us away by saying, "I know how to broadcast on TV around the school and neighborhood on a cable station here in town." We were really psyched.

The next day he says, "Okay, what do you want to broadcast?"

I said, "How about a newscast about what's going down here at school?" Everybody liked the idea, so Mr. Clifton made the arrangements with the cable station and the three of us put together a news show. Like, totally professional.

Saturday came and it's time to do the show and it's live. Yeah, well . . . we were all nervous but we were totally ready. So Mr. Clifton counts backwards from five and when he gets to zero, we're on the air! Miriam did news about school and tests and Terryl did upcoming events and Miriam came back with a little gossip and then I did the sports. It was awesome.

When we get to the end, Mr. Clifton is waving his arms like a monkey. We still had four minutes left. Hey, you talk about panic. Well, we just started faking it and making faces and I did a barking dog and a water faucet dripping. Then we got up and danced. Not a perfect show, but way fun.

We do the show every week. Tune in. It's Saturdays at three to three-thirty on Channel 27. Not a great time slot, but everybody likes it. I think it's because we keep in the dancing.

ABOUT THE AUTHOR

Raf Mauro is an actor, writer, and director. This is his third book of monologues for young actors. His sources for this audition material are real-life experiences, based all, or in part, on true-life situations. Some are taken from his own life and some from children he's known or observed. Many of his monologues are based upon the life experiences of his foster son, Andre Diamond. Andre and Raf run the Magic Mirror, an interactive, improvisational, children's show that has been operating since 1991 at the Third Stage Theater in Burbank, California. The Magic Mirror, which plays in schools all over Southern California, is interactive and built on the premise that the imagination is king. Children who see this show have their fertile imaginations challenged. This interactiveness and the improvisational nature of the show guarantees involvement, and affords children the opportunity of realizing that they can have power over that which entertains them. The more children experience the joy of Magic Mirror, the more they realize that inside the Magic Mirror everything is possible. Magic Mirror has been packaged for Las Vegas and television.

ORDER DIRECT

MONOLOGUES THEY HAVEN'T HEARD, Karshner. Speeches for men and women. $8.95.

MORE MONOLOGUES HAVEN'T HEARD, Karshner. More living-language speeches. $8.95.

SCENES THEY HAVEN'T SEEN, Karshner. Modern scenes for men and women. $7.95.

FOR WOMEN: MONOLOGUES THEY HAVEN'T HEARD, Pomerance. $8.95.

MONOLOGUES for KIDS, Roddy. 28 wonderful speeches for boys and girls. $8.95.

MORE MONOLOGUES for KIDS, Roddy. More great speeches for boys and girls. $8.95.

SCENES for KIDS, Roddy. 30 scenes for girls and boys. $8.95.

MONOLOGUES for TEENAGERS, Karshner. Contemporary teen speeches. $8.95.

SCENES for TEENAGERS, Karshner. Scenes for today's teen boys and girls. $8.95.

HIGH-SCHOOL MONOLOGUES THEY HAVEN'T HEARD, Karshner. $7.95.

MONOLOGUES from the CLASSICS, ed. Karshner. Speeches from Shakespeare, Marlowe, and others. An excellent collection for men and women, $8.95.

SHAKESPEARE'S MONOLOGUES THEY HAVEN'T HEARD, ed. Dotterer. Lesser-known speeches from The Bard. $7.95.

MONOLOGUES from CHEKHOV, trans. Cartwright. Modern translations from Chekhov's major plays: *Cherry Orchard, Uncle Vanya, Three Sisters, The Sea Gull.* $8.95.

MONOLOGUES from GEORGE BERNARD SHAW, ed. Michaels. Great speeches for men and women from the works of G.B.S. $7.95.

MONOLOGUES from OSCAR WILDE, ed. Michaels. The best of Wilde's urbane, dramatic writing from his greatest plays. For men and women. $7.95.

WOMAN, Pomerance. Monologues for actresses. $8.95.

MODERN SCENES for WOMEN, Pomerance. Scenes for today's actresses. $7.95.

MONOLOGUES from MOLIERE, trans. Dotterer. A definitive collection of speeches from the French Master. The first translation into English prose. $9.95.

SHAKESPEARE'S MONOLOGUES for WOMEN, ed. Dotterer. $8.95.

DIALECT MONOLOGUES, Karshner/Stern.13 essential dialects applied to contemporary monologues. Book and cassette tape. $19.95.

YOU SAID a MOUTHFUL, Karshner. Tongue twisters galore. Great exercises for actors, singers, public speakers. Fun for everyone. $8.95.

TEENAGE MOUTH, Karshner. Modern monologues for young men and women. $8.95.

SHAKESPEARE'S LADIES, ed. Dtterer. A second book of Shakespeare's monologues for women. With a descriptive text on acting Shakespeare. $7.95.

BETH HENLEY: MONOLOGUES for WOMEN, Henley.*Crimes of the Heart*, others. $7.95.

CITY WOMEN, Smith. 20 powerful, urban monologues. Great audition pieces. $7.95.

KIDS' STUFF, Roddy. 30 great audition pieces for children. $7.95.

KNAVES, KNIGHTS, and KINGS, ed. Dotterer. Shakespeare's speeches for men. $8.95.

DIALECT MONOLOUES, VOL II, Karshner/Stern. 14 more important dialects. Farsi, Afrikaans, Asian Indian, etc. Book and cassette tape. $19.95.

RED LICORICE, Tippit. 31 great scene-monologues for preteens. $8.95.

MODERN MONOLOGUES for MODERN KIDS, Mauro. $7.95.

SPEECHES and SCENES from OSCAR'S BEST FILMS, ed. Dotterer. $19.95.

A WOMAN SPEAKS: WOMEN FAMOUS, INFAMOUS and UNKNOWN, ed. Cosentio.$9.9.5

FITTING IN. Monologues for kids, Mauro. $8.95.

VOICES. Speeches from writings of famous women, ed. Cosentino. $9.95.

FOR WOMEN: MORE MONOS THEY HAVEN'T HEARD, Pomerance. $8.95.

NEIL SIMON MONOLOGUES. From the plays of America's foremost playwright. $10.95.

CLASSIC MOUTH, ed. Cosentino. Speeches for kids from famous literature. $8.95.

POCKET MONOLOGUES for WOMEN, Pomerance. 30 modern speeches. $8.95.

WHEN KINDS ACHIEVE, Mauro. Positive monologues for preteen boys and girls. $8.95.